Printed and Published in Great Britain by D. C. THOMSON & CO., LTD., 185 Fleet Street, London EC4 2

Bubble trouble!

SPOT THE SLIPPER

DENNIS HAS HIDDEN DAD'S SUPPLY OF 20 WHACKING SLIPPERS—CAN YOU FIND THEM ?

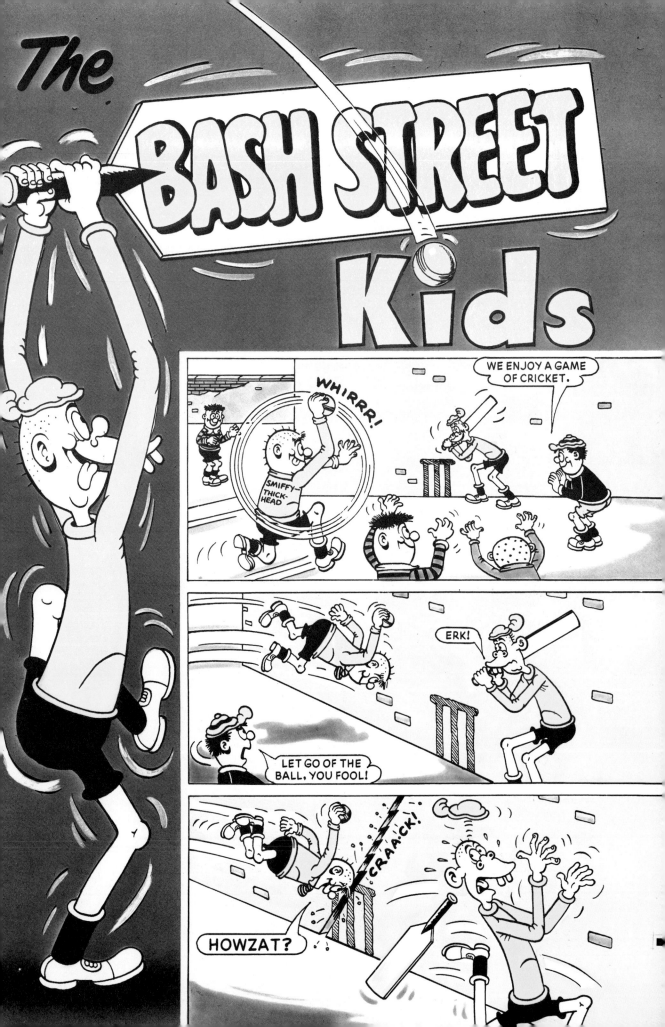

Silly fool closes school!

Brush off—from a toff!

Hip-hooray—holiday!

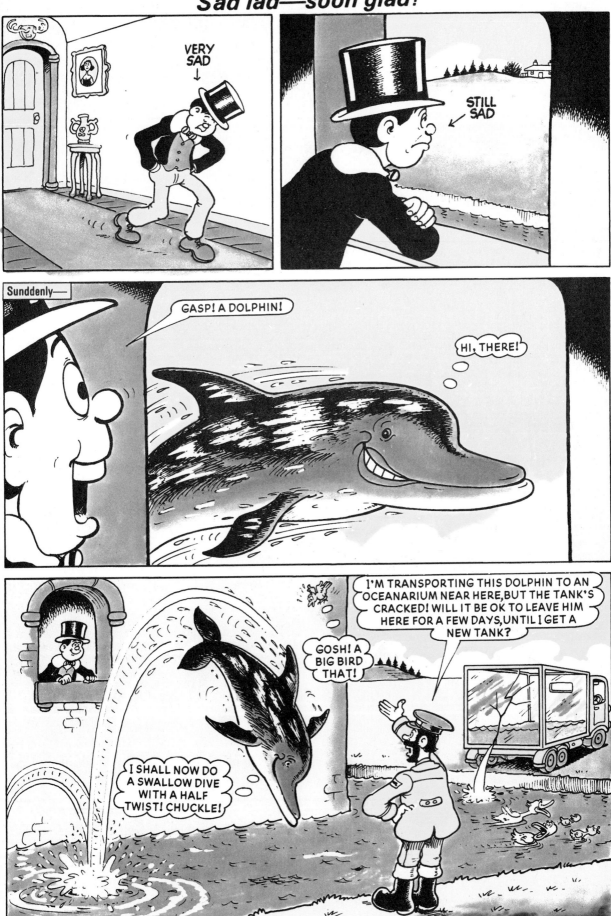

Below you'll see a letter for B.B.!

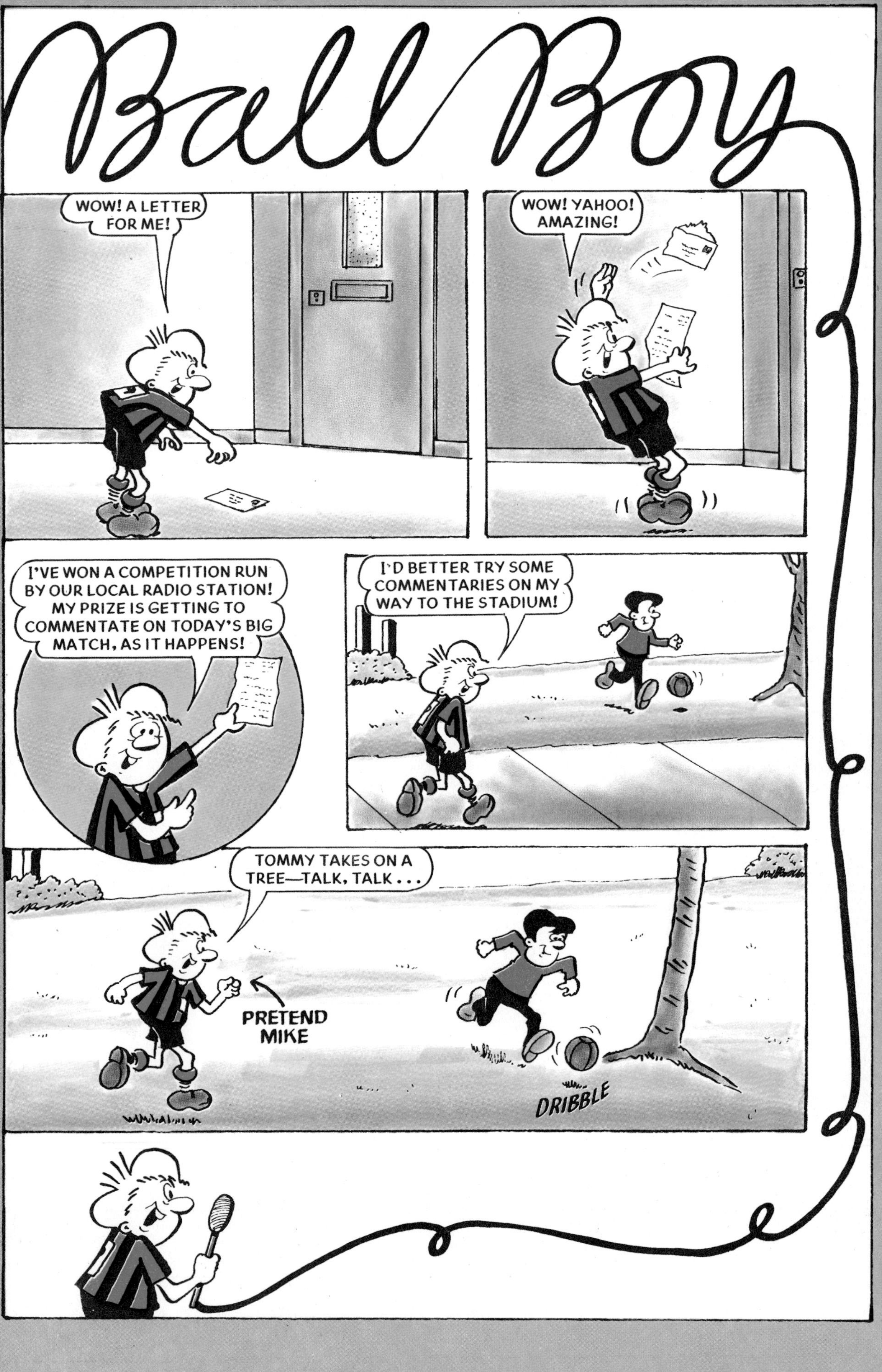

Look at the note Ball Boy wrote!

You just can't beat um ringside seat!

On the floor after tricks galore!

Oh, gosh! What a wash!

A Menace—but not Dennis!

High and dry!

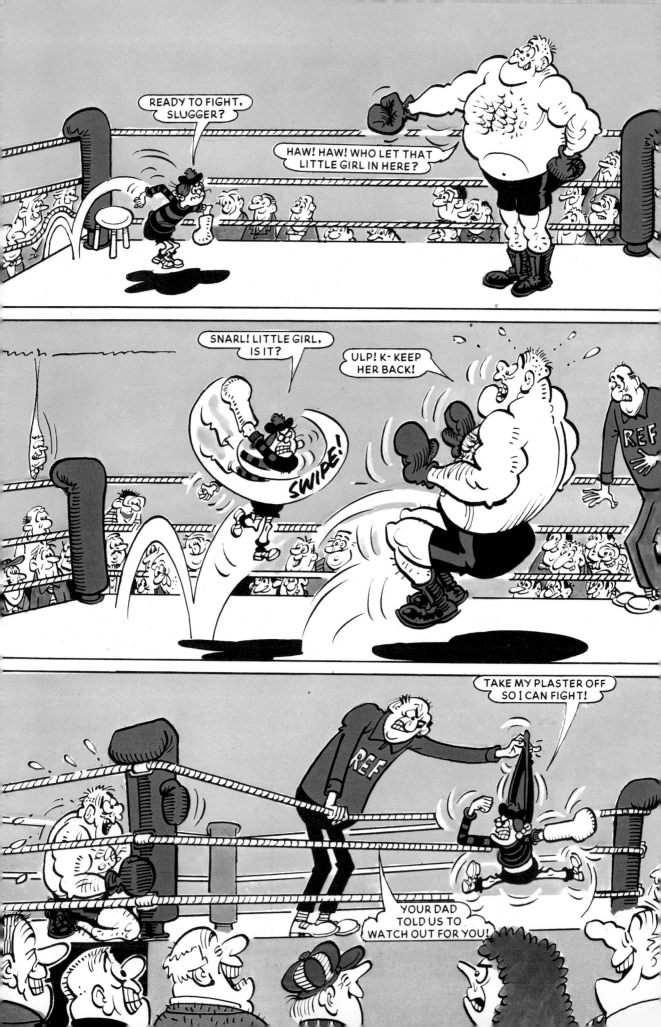

Here's a shock for the Doc!

An invite in flight!

The apple, of course, is for Plum's horse.

Never seen the like on an exercise bike!

Loose lace—sore face!

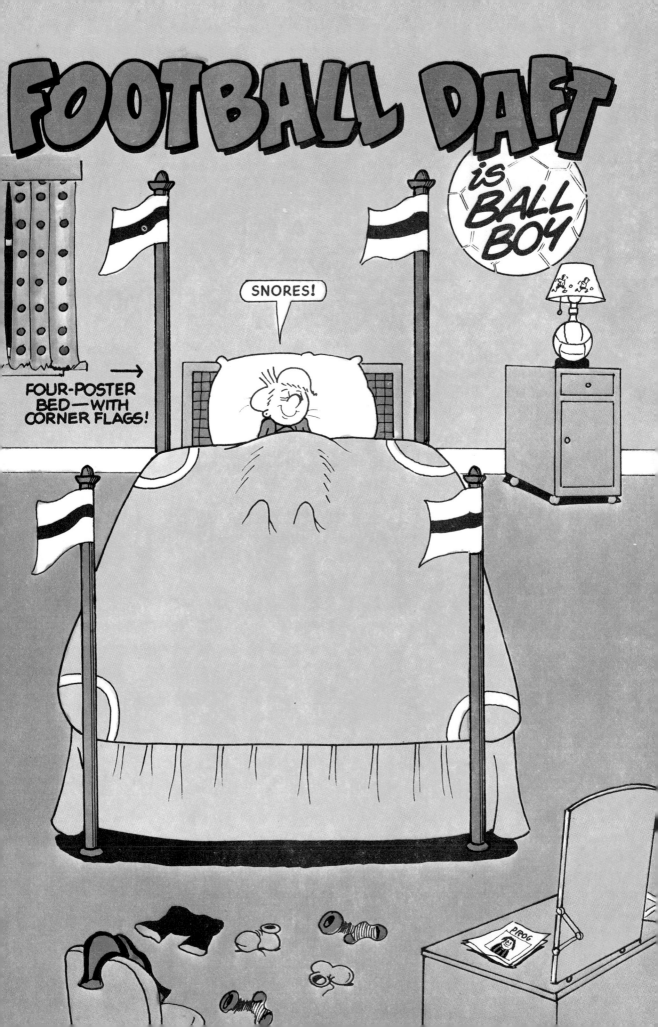

Tut-tut! Tough nut!

Grub galore—on the floor!

Have a look at this strange dodge book!

Soap slope!

For goodness sake—just one flake!

Rise surprise!